# CROC & ROLL

Mission Log: Louisiana, USA. Crocodile country!
CROC & ROLL
Ha! Ha! Action Man! Will the crocodile eat you, or will I fry you first?
Just what I need! Another lunatic!

# ACTION MAN

# COUNCIL OF DOOM

50p

24 hours before, a satellite was blown out of orbit by a violent electrical storm...
FZZZAKKK!
...it landed in the crocodile-ridden swamps of Louisiana.
Perfect for my new **Crocodile Mission**.
My tracker is telling me the satellite's nearby.
VREET! VREET!

Better have a look round...
SHRAAKK!
Aargh!
SHRAAKK!
We meet again, Action Man! Remember me? **Tempest**, master of storms!

I'll get you!
SHRAAKK!
Aargh!
I made the satellite crash land! Its secrets will be mine!
Ha! Ha! It's either my lightning or the crocodiles' jaws for you, Action Man!
Caught in the middle!
I could be served for dinner, unless...

...the **Crocodile Mission** has a homing device and a remote missile launcher!
CHOOOSH!
That won't hurt the crocs, but it'll keep them busy for a while.
SH...KOOM!
Now, to show Tempest what a sorry shower he is!
No chance, Action Man!

I hope you like hot food, Action Man!
Action Man dives!
This guy is just a **flash in the pan!**
Come back, I'll give you a **warm** welcome!
Time to cool this hothead down.
BEEP! BEEP!

Action Man blasts off the satellite...
SHAAKK!
WHOOSS!
The satellite! Nooo!
Aaiiee!
PLOSSHH!
SPLASSHH!
Watch out, Tempest! Electricity and water don't mix!
He's gone for now...
...but is that the last we'll see of him?
End

# SKY JACKED!

SKYJACKED!
Mission Log: Action Man has to make a dangerous delivery in Air Force jet **Thunderstreak**.
We're delivering the cargo in mid-air? That sounds dangerous.
I can handle it!
Cruising at 30,000 feet...
Altitude is vital for our cargo of precious mineral. Hey – that's another plane over there!

Relax, it's just the refuelling jet.
FUEL
That's no fuel hose! Break away!
This is a **flying** visit, Action Man!
SH-DUNK!
Too late!

Don't take a seat, X! You're going down!
I know you have the mineral. It can turn cheap metals into gold. It must be mine!
STRIDENIUM
Here's the emergency exit, Dr X!
Uggn!

KLEK!
Hey – what does this button do?
The pilot had to fly!
Aargh!
CHOOOOOT
Mind the open cockpit – you could get sucked out!
What are you doing?!
Have a nice trip, Action Man!
Aaarh!

X was too busy to notice my **air surfer**!
Oh no! The jet is heading for the city.
Can I make it into the cockpit?

Meanwhile, Dr X's jet begins its descent with the stolen stridenium on board...
Is this a good idea, boss?
Shut up! Open this container. I must see the mineral!
STR
On Action Man's jet...
This dive's too steep!
Got to get her nose up!

Later, on X's jet...
Yes! Made it!
I wouldn't open that container if I were you, X!
Action Man! But how?
Did you know the mineral is highly unstable? Below the height of 30,000 feet it shouldn't be exposed to the air...
...otherwise it disappears in a cloud of worthless, smelly gas!
Noo! *Kaf!*
But you'd have to be a real **airhead** to do something like that, right X?
Curse you, Action Man!
End

# TERRAIN OF TERROR!

TERRAIN OF TERROR!
Mission Log: Dr X has been traced to his mountain stronghold – **Castle X**. Up winding mountain paths, only Action Man's **ultra bike** can reach the castle.
There he is! Squash him to pulp, you fools!
Looks like Dr X has sent a welcoming party out to greet me!
RUMBLE
CRASH!

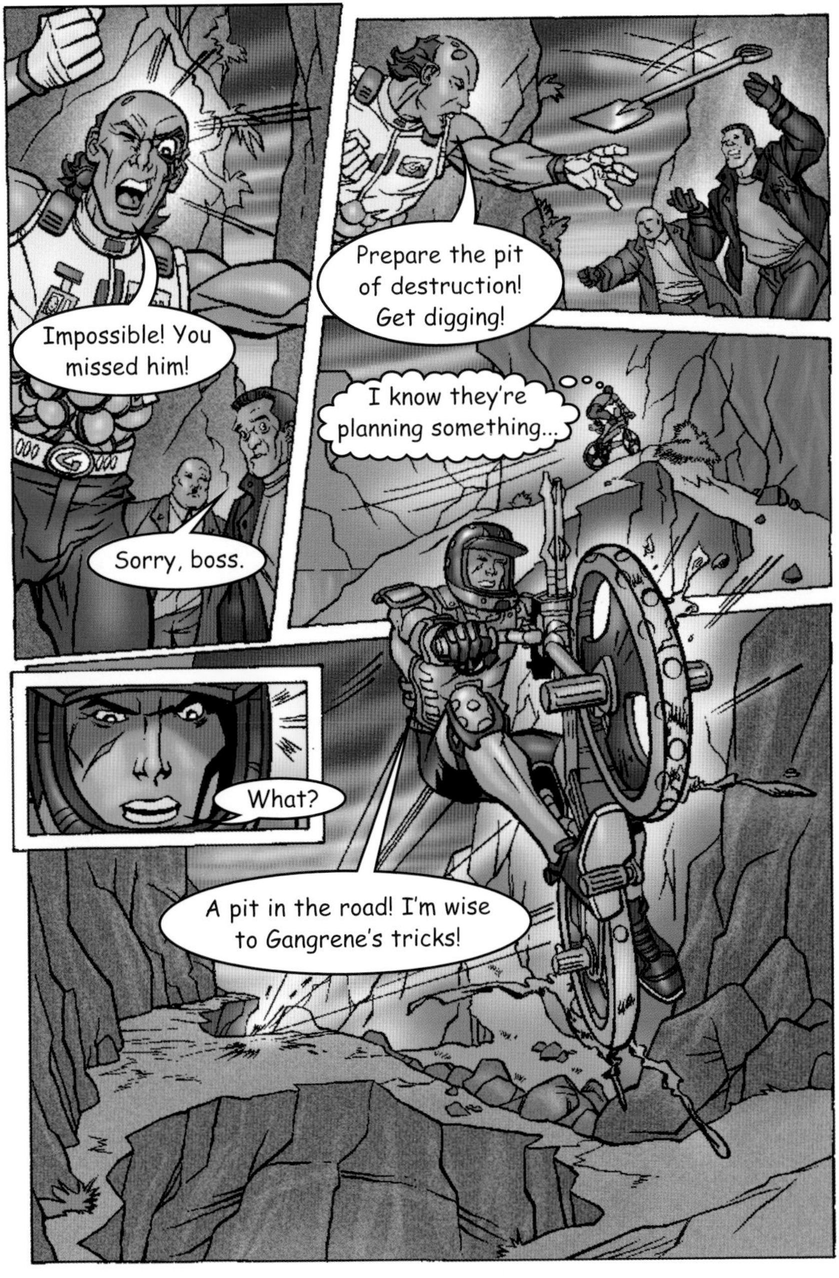
Impossible! You missed him!
Sorry, boss.
Prepare the pit of destruction! Get digging!
I know they're planning something...
What?
A pit in the road! I'm wise to Gangrene's tricks!

What's that up ahead?
That trip wire could have taken my head off!
I don't believe it! He's still alive!
Well, get him!

Woah, I don't want a puncture!
This toxic soup should stop him!
Nice one, boss!
SLOOSH!
Oof! That stuff doesn't look healthy!
SPLOOSH!
I'd better take the scenic route!
HISSS

Has Action Man escaped?
No, I'm right here, Gangrene!
Gah!
Oof!
Curse you, Action Man!
Catch you later – I can see you're **all tied up** right now!

That fool Gangrene should be back by now.
Er, there's something you should see!
Action Man is tearing towards the castle!
Quick! Raise the drawbridge!
I've only got one chance!
Bull's eye!
KATHUNK!

Aren't you pleased to see me, X?
Run, you fools!
Coming, ready or not!
THWOOM!
Look out!
Ha! You missed! Get him!
RRRUMBLE!
Before they can charge, the portcullis falls.
You'll pay for this!
You'll be behind bars for a long time, X!
End